Schirmer's Library of Musical Classics

Vol. 318

LOUIS KÖHLER

THE

EASIEST STUDIES

FOR THE

PIANO

Op. 151

PRELIMINARY TO THE AUTHOR'S
FIRST STUDIES, Op. 50

NEW YORK: G. SCHIRMER

1895

PREFACE.

In order to enable beginners in pianoforte-playing to devote themselves as early as possible to the acquirement of a smoothly flowing style of touch, I have composed the following little studies, which, of all those of their kind hitherto published, may, I think, be considered the easiest.

They are intended to lead to my Op. 50 (entitled "The first Studies, forming a basis of execution"), and should be presented to the pupil as soon as he can play with methodical correctness (even though but slowly), *and with a quiet hand*, the first five-finger exercises ; knows all the notes on the "great staff of 11 lines"—*i. e.:*

F to F and has attempted some easy little pieces for beginners. We may in addition continue to impart, gradually, such other elementary knowledge as may be found necessary for immediate practical use ; and should on no account neglect the daily practice of the scales, and the following important mechanical finger-exercises (useful even to more advanced players):

Each of these should be played with firmness and decision, by each hand separately, for one or two minutes. The scales should each be played 30, 50, or even 100 times ; at first by each hand separately, and only later with both hands together. When C major goes smoothly and correctly and the pupil has been through all the major scales several times (which would perhaps take up the first year of study), a new one, or a pair of new ones, may be practised daily in the following order :—C major and A minor ; G major and E minor ; D major and B minor ; A and F♯ ; E and C♯ ; B and G♯ ; F♯ (G♭) and D♯ (E♭) ; C♯ (D♭) and A♯ (B♭) ; A♭ and F ; E♭ and C ; B♭ and G ; F and D ; and after this again from the beginning.

In the following little studies (each of which contains 32 bars in the same key and time) a principal part, in eighth-notes, is given to each hand alternately ; and each pair of studies is so arranged that melodic progression by degree alternates with that by skip, continually.

While practising, the principal part should always first be taken with the one hand, and played in comfortable, easy time (no matter how slowly) until it is played properly, smoothly, and without exertion. Each study may, if desired, be divided into groups of eight or sixteen bars, and such small portions repeated over and over again, in order to impress them upon the memory ; so that the eyes, requiring to be less exclusively fixed upon the written notes, may be free to attend to the position of the hands and fingers. The more easy part, that for the other hand, should be played only now and then for a change, and always in proper relative time ; only when each hand is quite perfect are both hands to be practised together, and at first just as slowly as the separate parts have previously been played.

When one study is almost perfect, the principal part of the next one may be begun single handed, but the subordinate part (for the other hand) must not be touched until the previous study is completely mastered. This manner of practising may be recommended, even to more advanced players, as the surest, safest and consequently the shortest way to the desired end.

The utmost care should be taken while playing, to maintain the right position of the hands and fingers. The finger-tip should be elevated fully as high as the black keys. The stroke should be delivered after quiet consideration, quite suddenly, with decision, *without any other movement of the hand*, and without bending the knuckles. The pressure of the finger on the key should be firm, but not rigid or cramped, and should be maintained at the same power until the next finger delivers its own stroke, when it should be swiftly lifted at precisely the same moment as its successor descends. Thus will a "soundful and songful" touch be formed. This refers more particularly to the studies based upon diatonic passages (progressing by 'degree') Nos. 1, 2 ; 5, 6 ; and 9, 10. In the others, based upon chords, the long holding-notes (those with two stems) must be carefully held down as indicated.

It is also useful to hold down each successive note of such chord-passages till the last note of each chord has been sounded, as, for instance, in No. 3, thus :— &c.

This will cultivate the extension of the fingers, familiarize the ear with the sound of the chords, and accustom the pupil to instinctively realize the amount of pressure requisite for the production of a good *legato.*

The speed must always be moderate and convenient. The volume of tone must depend upon the natural strength of the player, but should incline rather towards too much power than too little, and must always be equal.

LOUIS KÖHLER.

43 = 12T

Hodik Eg.

43 = 12

3

4

43 = 12

43=12

7

43 = 12

43 = 12

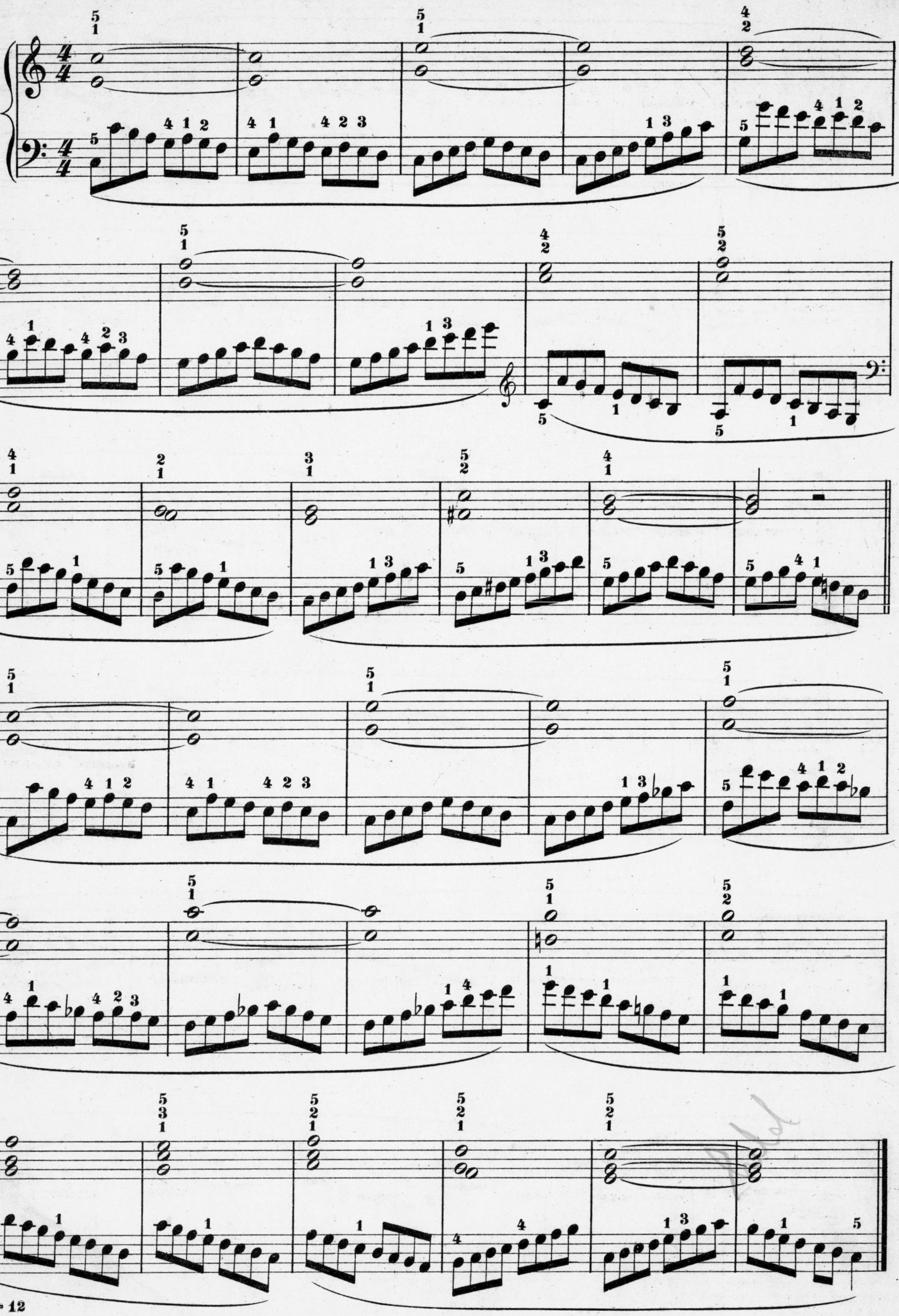

11